VISION DISCOVERY
journal

VISION DISCOVERY
journal

CARRIE PICKETT

Published in partnership between Andrew Wommack Ministries and Harrison House Publishers

Shippensburg, PA 17257

ISBN 13 TP: 978-1-5954-8567-0

For Worldwide Distribution, Printed in the U.S.A.

1 2 3 4 5 6 7 8 / 27 26 25 24 23

To those who are willing to obey and trust that God's love, lived through them, can change the world.

Foreword

Vision—a word that holds limitless possibilities. It's a word that can keep you up at night and urge you along in the morning. It expresses that it's something to be seen. It evokes a passion and a pursuit. Vision causes your character, personality, purpose, giftings, and talents to collide into a movement that everyone around you recognizes as destiny.

This destiny you surrender to becomes a lifelong process of growth and fruit that starts to impact and influence people along the way.

Herein lies the amazing potential of being a person with a vision. Life becomes bigger than the canvas of your own life. You now possess the urgency to express your God-given ambitions and giftings knowing that God wants to reveal Himself through them. We tend to make vision about ourselves when, in true definition, it is "seeing" God's plan for us and uniquely living that plan out. God has already placed that vision and plan in you long before you were born.

How exciting! You are now invited into a relationship with God that involves the discovery of His plan for you. It is always bigger than what we think is possible—that's why it is a God-plan.

In the discovery process comes a daily opportunity to believe. Do you believe God is big enough to accomplish the vision emerging from your heart? Better yet, will you believe that someone like you can be used by God? This is where most people get caught up. They have no sight or vision of how God truly sees them.

This is why your relationship with God should be your main pursuit. It's not what you do for Him. It's who you allow Him to be in you, and who you become for Him out of that relationship.

When you see how big God is, the power of His promises, and the depths of His unfailing love toward you, you realize nothing is impossible to him who believes!

Now, it's learning to mine what God deposited in you when you were created. It is key to realize that His love for us is bigger than our current comfort level. Your capacity for vision is based on how much you allow the love of God to have place within your life.

Big vision requires deep connection to God. That is where it's birthed, taught, equipped, fashioned, timed, and released. The source of your vision is where the capacity and power to accomplish it reside.

Don't just believe—obey. At the end of the day, God can show you a picture and a path, but it's only your obedience that will start you on the journey. Obedience is not just in the first step, it's a lifestyle.

Believe that by you saying "yes," it changes people's lives. Your obedience now becomes a pathway for God to reveal His glory and love. What a joy to be called to the eternal vision of God for this world. As you say "yes," you must understand that obedience requires growth and change. You can't stay the way you are and accomplish greater things.

Through this journal, allow the Holy Spirit to lead you into discovering who God has made you and what He has placed in front of you to become and do. During the discovery, understand that He's showing you things to do now and for the future. Knowing the difference comes by discovering what season you are in and what you need to grow in. This will help you arrive at those future plans God has for you.

As you fill in the pages of this journal, don't become stressed. It's a journey with God. Invite Him to help you fill in the pages. As a believer, your life now belongs to Christ. Therefore, He knows how to live it best!

Enjoy the discovery, surrender, obedience, and joy of walking in your vision!

*"You make yourself intentional by
asking yourself tough questions."*

John Maxwell

"What would you attempt to do if you knew you would not fail?"

Robert H. Schuller

How would you describe the strength of your relationship with God?

E

How would you describe the season of life you are in right now? How do you think God can use this season?

S

_____

_____

_____

_____

_____

_____

_____

_____

_____

_____

_____

_____

_____

_____

_____

_____

_____

_____

_____

_____

_____

_____

_____

_____

_____

_____

_____

_____

_____

_____

_____

_____

_____

_____

_____

_____

_____

_____

_____

_____

_____

_____

_____

_____

_____

_____

_____

_____

_____

_____

What life experiences, successes, failures, jobs, and relationships have prepared you for this season of your life?

_____

_____

_____

_____

_____

_____

_____

_____

_____

_____

_____

_____

_____

_____

_____

_____

_____

_____

_____

_____

_____

_____

_____

_____

_____

Do you believe God could use someone
like you? Describe why or why not.

_____
_____
_____
_____
_____
_____
_____
_____
_____
_____
_____
_____
_____
_____
_____
_____
_____
_____
_____
_____
_____
_____
_____
_____
_____

Are you surrendered enough in your relationship with God that He can lead and guide you into His purpose and vision? If not, what is holding you back?

Write down any lies you've believed that are holding you back. Next to each lie, write one truth that counters that lie.

What is a one key action you can take to
begin changing what is holding you back?

Describe the most impactful thing God has done in your life.

_____

_____

_____

_____

_____

_____

_____

_____

_____

_____

_____

_____

_____

_____

_____

_____

_____

_____

_____

_____

_____

_____

_____

_____

_____

_____

E

Describe your testimony. What parts of your story can you see impacting lives?

E

What is the one message you are most passionate about sharing with people?

S

_____

_____

_____

_____

_____

_____

_____

_____

_____

_____

_____

_____

_____

_____

_____

_____

_____

_____

_____

_____

_____

_____

_____

_____

_____

_____

_____

When you think of the future, what
brings excitement to your heart?

_____

_____

_____

_____

_____

_____

_____

_____

_____

_____

_____

_____

_____

_____

_____

_____

_____

_____

_____

_____

_____

_____

_____

_____

_____

What would you do or who would you become
if you couldn't fail? Allow yourself to dream!

_____

_____

_____

_____

_____

_____

_____

_____

_____

_____

_____

_____

_____

_____

_____

_____

_____

_____

_____

_____

_____

_____

Write down words that inspire you with purpose and vision. Next to each word, describe why it inspires you.

E

Who or what do you want to impact in your life? Is there a certain demographic or issue you want to influence? What stirs or excites your heart about that demographic or issue?

S

_____

_____

_____

_____

_____

_____

_____

_____

_____

_____

_____

_____

_____

_____

_____

_____

_____

_____

_____

_____

_____

_____

_____

_____

_____

_____

_____

_____

_____

_____

Who inspires you?
What about them inspires you?

What can you learn from them and
apply to your life today?

_____
_____
_____
_____
_____
_____
_____
_____
_____
_____
_____
_____
_____
_____
_____
_____
_____
_____
_____
_____
_____
_____
_____

Are there current commitments or responsibilities in your life that need to shift for you to step into new areas of your vision and purpose?

What distractions are keeping you from walking in your strengths, calling, and purpose?

E

Write one distraction you can
begin to eliminate and how.

S _____
_____
_____
_____
_____
_____
_____
_____
_____
_____
_____
_____
_____
_____
_____
_____
_____
_____
_____
_____
_____
_____
_____
_____
_____
_____
_____

In what areas are you comparing yourself
to others? Do you feel that comparison
is holding you back? If so, how?

What are you currently doing to become more skilled in the areas you're interested in?

What strengths can you identify in yourself that haven't been developed? What steps can you take to develop those strengths?

What do you think will happen if you
start investing in your strengths?

_____
_____
_____
_____
_____
_____
_____
_____
_____
_____
_____
_____
_____
_____
_____
_____
_____
_____
_____
_____
_____
_____
_____
_____
_____

What is the biggest strength you bring to the lives around you?

How do you feel your strengths are
impacting the lives around you?

_____

_____

_____

_____

_____

_____

_____

_____

_____

_____

_____

_____

_____

_____

_____

_____

_____

_____

_____

_____

_____

_____

_____

_____

How can you keep yourself from becoming prideful or careless with your strengths?

_____
_____
_____
_____
_____
_____
_____
_____
_____
_____
_____
_____
_____
_____
_____
_____
_____
_____
_____
_____
_____
_____
_____
_____
_____
_____
_____
_____

Do you have strengths that you feel weaken your impact? If so, how?

_____
_____
_____
_____
_____
_____
_____
_____
_____
_____
_____
_____
_____
_____
_____
_____
_____
_____
_____
_____
_____
_____
_____
_____
_____
_____
_____

What is the biggest weakness you bring to the lives around you?

How do you feel your weaknesses are impacting the lives around you?

If you were to surrender your strengths
and weaknesses to God, how do you
think He could use them?

Where do you want to be in a year from now?

E

What is God leading you to do in the next year?

S

E

What changes do you need to make to get to that place in a year? Write out your next steps to follow through.

S

Where do you want to be in three years from now? Allow yourself to dream about the next three years and write down what that could look like.

Where do you see yourself in five years? Allow yourself to dream about the next five years and write down what that could look like.

Where do you see yourself in ten years? Allow yourself to dream about the next ten years and write down what that could look like.

_____

_____

_____

_____

_____

_____

_____

_____

_____

_____

_____

_____

_____

_____

_____

_____

_____

_____

_____

_____

_____

_____

_____

_____

_____

_____

_____

_____

_____

_____

What area of your life do you need to be obedient to God in?

E

If you were to say "yes" to whatever God is leading
you to do right now, what would that look like?

S _____
_____
_____
_____
_____
_____
_____
_____
_____
_____
_____
_____
_____
_____
_____
_____
_____
_____
_____
_____
_____
_____
_____
_____
_____
_____
_____
_____

If you were to say "yes" to God's plan for your life, who do you think your life would touch?

What do you feel the Lord is prompting you to change?

S

What is the most common excuse you find
yourself saying? How can you eliminate
that excuse from your vocabulary?

_____

_____

_____

_____

_____

_____

_____

_____

_____

_____

_____

_____

_____

_____

_____

_____

_____

_____

_____

_____

_____

_____

_____

_____

What system of accountability do you have in your life to help you achieve the goals God has given you?

S

E

What are some practical ways you can invest in your growth?

S

What are you currently reading or studying
to see change happen in your life?

S

E

What quotes are you meditating on? Why
do you meditate on those quotes?

S _____

_____

_____

_____

_____

_____

_____

_____

_____

_____

_____

_____

_____

_____

_____

_____

_____

_____

_____

_____

_____

_____

_____

What ideas are you currently researching or developing and why?

When presented with information, lessons, or counsel from others, how do you apply it to your life?

Do you have a process? If not, what is a process that could work for you?

_____
_____
_____
_____
_____
_____
_____
_____
_____
_____
_____
_____
_____
_____
_____
_____
_____
_____
_____

What changes do you need to make in your daily schedule to accomplish your goals this season? Write down what your schedule needs to look like.

Which relationships in your life need strengthening to move forward with the vision God has given you?

_____
_____
_____
_____
_____
_____
_____
_____
_____
_____
_____
_____
_____
_____
_____
_____
_____
_____
_____
_____
_____
_____
_____
_____
_____
_____
_____

What are some practical ways you can intentionally strengthen those relationships?

_____

_____

_____

_____

_____

_____

_____

_____

_____

_____

_____

_____

_____

_____

_____

_____

_____

_____

_____

_____

_____

_____

What relationships in your life are keeping
you from moving forward with the vision God
has given you? What steps or conversations
need to take place in those relationships?

_____
_____
_____
_____
_____
_____
_____
_____
_____
_____
_____
_____
_____
_____
_____
_____
_____
_____
_____
_____
_____

Describe what you are learning from mentors in your life. (Including mentorships in person and mentorships through media by ministers, teachers, authors, etc.)

_____
_____
_____
_____
_____
_____
_____
_____
_____
_____
_____
_____
_____
_____
_____
_____
_____
_____
_____
_____
_____
_____
_____

_____
_____
_____
_____
_____
_____
_____
_____
_____
_____
_____
_____
_____
_____
_____
_____
_____
_____
_____
_____
_____
_____
_____
_____
_____
_____
_____
_____
_____
_____
_____
_____

Are you prioritizing your rest and health? If not, what steps can you take to prioritize your rest and health?

_____
_____
_____
_____
_____
_____
_____
_____
_____
_____
_____
_____
_____
_____
_____
_____
_____
_____
_____
_____
_____
_____
_____
_____
_____
_____
_____
_____
_____
_____
_____
_____
_____

Where do you want your health and strength to be in three, five, and ten years? What are some practical ways you can reach your goals?

How do you want the key relationships in your life to look like in three, five, and ten years?

If you are not married, what do you want your future marriage to look like? If you are married, what changes do you want to make in your marriage?

_____
_____
_____
_____
_____
_____
_____
_____
_____
_____
_____
_____
_____
_____
_____
_____
_____
_____
_____
_____
_____
_____
_____
_____
_____
_____

If you are married, how can you improve your
communication and intimacy with your spouse?

_____

_____

_____

_____

_____

_____

_____

_____

_____

_____

_____

_____

_____

_____

_____

_____

_____

_____

_____

_____

_____

_____

_____

_____

_____

_____

If you have children, how are you prioritizing developing, spending time, and communicating with them?

If you have children, how can you help them discover and begin walking in the vision God has for them?

If you have children, ask them what their dreams are. Now, describe how you and your family can begin to support those dreams in the coming years.

Do you find yourself saying "someday" or "tomorrow" when thinking of your purpose and vision? How can you change this?

_____

_____

_____

_____

_____

_____

_____

_____

_____

_____

_____

_____

_____

_____

_____

_____

_____

_____

_____

_____

_____

_____

_____

_____

_____

_____

_____

_____

_____

_____

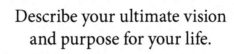

Describe your ultimate vision
and purpose for your life.

_____

_____

_____

_____

_____

_____

_____

_____

_____

_____

_____

_____

_____

_____

_____

_____

_____

_____

_____

_____

_____

_____

_____

_____

_____

_____

E

What is one action you can take today to step toward the vision God is calling you to?

S _____
_____
_____
_____
_____
_____
_____
_____
_____
_____
_____
_____
_____
_____
_____
_____
_____
_____
_____
_____
_____
_____
_____
_____
_____
_____

Receive Jesus as Your Savior

Choosing to receive Jesus Christ as your Lord and Savior is the most important decision you'll ever make!

God's Word promises, *"That if thou shalt confess with thy mouth the Lord Jesus, and shalt believe in thine heart that God hath raised him from the dead, thou shalt be saved. For with the heart man believeth unto righteousness; and with the mouth confession is made unto salvation"* (Rom. 10:9–10). *"For whosoever shall call upon the name of the Lord shall be saved"* (Rom. 10:13). By His grace, God has already done everything to provide salvation. Your part is simply to believe and receive.

Pray out loud: "Jesus, I confess that You are my Lord and Savior. I believe in my heart that God raised You from the dead. By faith in Your Word, I receive salvation now. Thank You for saving me."

The very moment you commit your life to Jesus Christ, the truth of His Word instantly comes to pass in your spirit. Now that you're born again, there's a brand-new you!

Receive the Holy Spirit

As His child, your loving heavenly Father wants to give you the supernatural power you need to live a new life. *"For every one that asketh receiveth; and he that seeketh findeth; and to him that knocketh it shall be opened…how much more shall your heavenly Father give the Holy Spirit to them that ask him?"* (Luke 11:10–13).

All you have to do is ask, believe, and receive!

Pray this: "Father, I recognize my need for Your power to live a new life. Please fill me with Your Holy Spirit. By faith, I receive it right now. Thank You for baptizing me. Holy Spirit, You are welcome in my life."

Congratulations! Now you're filled with God's supernatural power.

Some syllables from a language you don't recognize will rise up from your heart to your mouth (1 Cor. 14:14). As you speak them out loud by faith, you're releasing God's power from within and building yourself up in the spirit (1 Cor. 14:4). You can do this whenever and wherever you like.

It doesn't really matter whether you felt anything or not when you prayed to receive the Lord and His Spirit. If you believed in your heart that you received, then God's Word promises you did. *"Therefore I say unto you, What things soever ye desire, when ye pray, believe that ye receive them, and ye shall have them"* (Mark 11:24). God always honors His Word—believe it!

Please contact me and let me know that you've prayed to receive Jesus as your Savior or be filled with the Holy Spirit. I would like to rejoice with you and help you understand more fully what has taken place in your life. I'll send you a free gift that will help you understand and grow in your new relationship with the Lord.

Welcome to your new life!

Call for Prayer

If you need prayer for any reason, you can call our Prayer Line 24 hours a day, seven days a week at 719-635-1111. A trained prayer minister will answer your call and pray with you. Every day, we receive testimonies of healings and other miracles from our Prayer Line, and we are ministering God's nearly-too-good-to-be-true message of the Gospel to more people than ever. So I encourage you to call today!

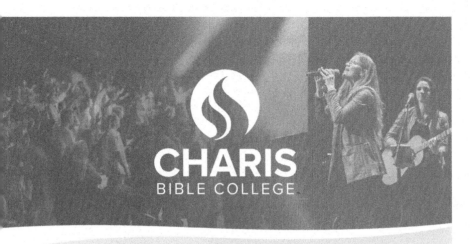

God has **more** for you.

Are you longing to find your God-given purpose? At Charis Bible College you will establish a firm foundation in the Word of God and receive hands-on ministry experience to **find, follow** and **fulfill** your purpose.

Scan the QR code to visit CharisBibleCollege.org

Admissions@awmcharis.com
(844) 360-9577

Change your life. **Change the world.**

life FOUNDATIONS
with Carrie Pickett

Join Carrie as she uncovers the foundational principles of the Word of God and discover how these truths can transform your everyday life.

Scan the QR code to watch full episodes of Life Foundations

CONTACT INFORMATION

Charis Bible College

800 Gospel Truth Way

Woodland Park, CO 80863

info@charisbiblecollege.org

Helpline Available 24/7: 719-635-1111

CharisBibleCollege.org

Also visit Carrie at CarriePickett.com